Steck-Vaughn
Berrent

Math
Problem Solving

- **Enhanced Multiple-Choice**
- **Free-Response**
- **Open-Ended**

by Francis J. Gardella, Ed. D.

About the Author:

Dr. Frank Gardella is Associate Professor of Mathematics Education at
Hunter College, City University of New York. His career in math education,
which spans more than thirty years, includes teaching and supervising in
both urban and suburban districts. Dr. Gardella has authored several books
and is a frequent speaker at regional and national conferences. Gail Gardella,
his wife, assisted him in the research of this book.

Executive Editor: Karen Bischoff

Project Editor: Louise Marinis

Assistant Editor: Caren Churchbuilder

Design Director: Frank Bruno

Illustrator: Katherine Schultz

Design & Layout: Rmedia Digital Imaging and Design

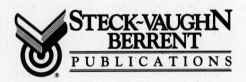

STECK-VAUGHN
BERRENT
PUBLICATIONS

Steck-Vaughn/Berrent Math Problem Solving

ISBN 0-8172-7590-8

Published by ©Steck-Vaughn/Berrent Publications, a division of Steck-Vaughn Company.

1 2 3 4 5 6 7 8 9   RP   03 02 01 00 99 98

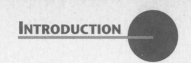

Math is all around us. We use it every day. When you tell time, you are using math. When you buy something, you are using math. When you walk home from school, you are using math.

Some of us think of math as hard to do. But if you practice doing math problems, it won't be so hard to do.

This book has been written to help you do well on math tests. It will give you practice answering problems.

When taking math tests, you will find three different kinds of problems.

■ **Multiple-choice problems**: These give you three answer choices to pick from after each problem.

■ **Free-response problems**: These do not have choices for you to pick from. You must fill in the answer on your own. There is only one answer to each problem.

■ **Open-ended problems**: These also do not have choices for you to pick from. Sometimes you need to do a lot of work to figure out the answer. Sometimes you need to draw a diagram or write a chart. Many times there is more than one correct answer to the question.

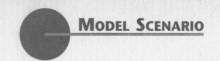
Teacher Read Aloud: Before you work on any math problems, there will be a story for you to read. Read this story about twins. Read it carefully. It will help you solve the problems.

Twins

Jesse and Jarad are twin brothers. They are 7 years old. Their sister Tasha is 15 years old.

Teacher Read Aloud: (After the picture are some multiple-choice questions.) Circle the correct answer to each question. Read the question and ALL the choices before picking your answer.

I. How old is Jarad?

a. older than Tasha

b. younger than Tasha

c. older than Jesse

Teacher Read Aloud: Here is a hint to help you. Read the story again. Write down how old Jesse, Jarad, and Tasha are. Then read the question and choices again. Which choice is the correct one?

2. How much older is Tasha than her brothers?

a. 7 years older

b. 8 years older

c. 9 years older

Teacher Read Aloud: Here is a hint to help you. Check the ages that you wrote down for problem I. Take away the age of the brothers from Tasha's age. Look for this number in the answer choices.

Teacher Read Aloud: The next problems do not give answer choices. You need to fill in the answer on your own. There is only one correct answer to these problems.

3. In how many years will Jesse and Jarad be 10 years old?

Teacher Read Aloud: Here is a hint to help you. Look to see how old Jesse and Jarad are now. Then count how many years there are until they are 10 years old.

4. How old will Tasha be in 6 years?

Teacher Read Aloud: Here is a hint to help you. Add 6 to Tasha's age. This will give you your answer.

5. Will Jesse and Jarad be 8 years old before Tasha is 17 years old?

Teacher Read Aloud: Here is a hint to help you. The answer to this question is "yes" or "no." Count how many years it will be for the brothers to turn 8. Count how many years it will be for Tasha to turn 17. Read the problem again. Now you can answer it.

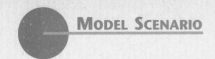

Teacher Read Aloud: **The last problems are work problems. They ask you to do more work than the other problems. Sometimes they will ask you to draw a picture or fill in a chart. Many times there is more than one correct answer to these problems.**

6. Tell why Tasha will always be the same number of years older than Jesse and Jarad.

Teacher Read Aloud: **Here is a hint to help you. You get to write a little for this problem. Try to figure out the answer to the problem in your head. Then write your answer. Write one or two sentences to answer the problem.**

The first key to solving math problems is to follow these steps.

THINK

Think about what the problem is asking you to do.

CHOOSE

Choose a strategy.

SOLVE

Solve the problem.

CHECK

Check your answer to make sure it's correct.

Patterns

Oscar drew a box with shapes in it. He made a pattern with the shapes. Here is Oscar's box.

1. Tell how many kinds of shapes are in the pattern.

   a. 2

   b. 3

   c. 4

2. Which shape is not in the pattern?

   a.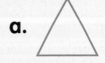

   b.

   c.

3. Oscar wants to copy this pattern for his sister. How many more circles does he need?

   a. 2

   b. 4

   c. 8

4. How many kinds of shapes in the pattern have 4 sides?

5. Oscar wants to copy the pattern for 2 friends. How many more shapes does he need to draw?

6. Draw the missing shape.

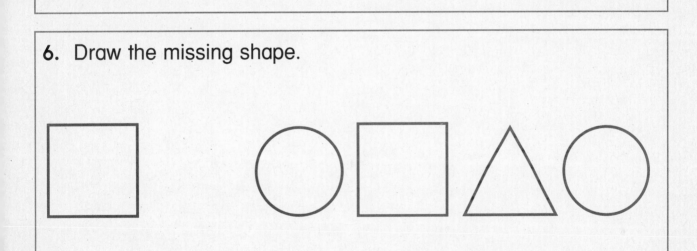

7. Draw a different pattern with Oscar's shapes.

8. Oscar adds a ☐ to the pattern. Draw what the pattern looks like now.

Taking Shape

Nadia cut out shapes and pasted them like this on a piece of paper.

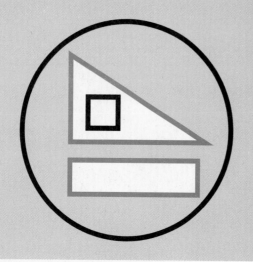

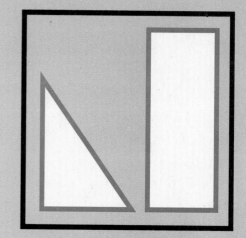

1. Which shape is not used?

a.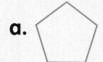

b.

c.

2. How many triangles are there in all?

  a. 1

  b. 2

  c. 3

3. What shape is inside the ?

  a. circle

  b. square

  c. triangle

4. Draw the biggest shape inside the circle.

5. How many more shapes are inside the big circle than inside the big square?

6. Draw the shape that is inside the circle, and under the triangle.

7. Draw a square with a triangle inside it.

8. Draw two triangles and a circle inside a rectangle.

Animal Parade

The animals are in line for the parade.

DONKEY   CHICK   TURTLE   DOG

I. Which animal faces to the right?

a. donkey

b. turtle

c. dog

2. Which animal shows a tail?

a. chick

b. donkey

c. turtle

3. Which animal is green?

a. dog

b. chick

c. donkey

4. The chick is removed from the parade. A cat is put in its place. How many legs are now in the parade?

5. Ronni has a picture of two animals from the parade. They have eight legs in all. Does each animal have 4 legs?

6. A tank with 5 fish joins the parade. How many more legs are there?

7. List the animals in the parade by size, from largest to smallest.

8. Draw 3 different animals that have 10 legs in all.

In the Bag

Jamie has a bag of coins. Here are the types of coins that are in her bag.

DIME   NICKEL   PENNY

I. Which is worth the most?

   a.

   b.

   c.

2. What is the value of a ?

   a. I penny

   b. 2 nickels

   c. 5 nickels

3. Jamie has 2I pennies. She trades as many of her pennies for nickels as she can. How many pennies does she have now?

   a. I

   b. 3

   c. 4

4. Jamie has 8 nickels. How many cents does she have?

5. Which is worth more, 2 dimes or 3 nickels?

6. Jamie has 3 dimes, 2 nickels, and 2 pennies in her bag. How much money is this in all?

7. Jamie buys a pencil for 28¢. Which coins does she use?

8. Jamie reaches into her bag and grabs 5 coins. How much money can she have?

Time Line

Tim draws a time line. On it he writes the times he does things during the day.

7:00 A.M.	9:00 A.M.	12:30 P.M.	1:30 P.M.	3:00 P.M.	6:00 P.M.
Wake Up	School Starts	Lunch	Math	School Ends	Dinner

l. What does Tim do at 1:30 P.M.?

   a. wake up

   b. eat lunch

   c. learn math

2. About what time does Tim walk to school?

   a. 8:30 A.M.

   b. 10:30 A.M.

   c. 3:30 P.M.

3. How long is lunch?

   a. half an hour

   b. one hour

   c. an hour and a half

4. What time does Tim wake up?

5. Write the latest time shown on Tim's time line.

6. How many hours pass from the beginning of lunch to the end of school?

7. Tim has reading before math. Put it on Tim's time line. Give a time for it.

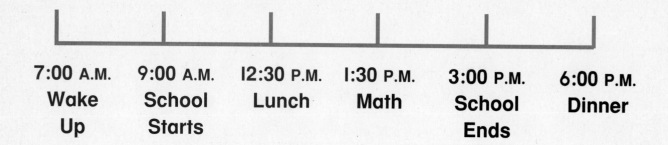

7:00 A.M. **9:00** A.M. **12:30** P.M. **1:30** P.M. **3:00** P.M. **6:00** P.M.

Wake   **School**   **Lunch**   **Math**   **School**   **Dinner**

Up   **Starts**   **Ends**

8. Monica goes to a different school. Here is her time line. Decide what times she has recess, lunch, and math. Then show each on her time line.

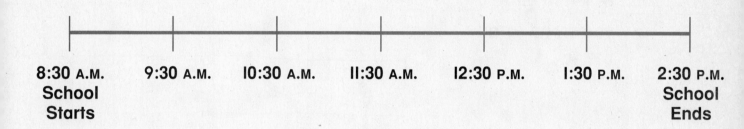

8:30 A.M.
School
Starts

9:30 A.M.

10:30 A.M.

11:30 A.M.

12:30 P.M.

1:30 P.M.

2:30 P.M.
School
Ends

Food Machine

The lunch room at school has a food machine. The pictures show what it holds inside. The numbers tell how many of each coin you need to buy the food.

FOOD	quarter	dime	nickel
apple	1	1	
banana	1	2	
pear	1	1	1
ORANGE JUICE	2	2	

1. A ⌒ costs
   a. 15¢
   b. 25¢
   c. 45¢

2. What can you buy with 1 and 1 ?
   a. apple
   b. pear
   c. banana

3. Which coins will buy ?
   a. (dime, nickel, nickel)
   b. (quarter, dime, dime)
   c. (quarter, quarter, dime, dime)

4. Tad puts   into the machine. Draw what he buys?

5. What can you buy if you have   ?

6. Myra uses 2 coins to buy I thing from the food machine. What does she buy?

7. A food machine at the bus stop has higher prices. Show the prices and the number of each coin needed to buy each item.

FOOD	PRICE			

8. One food machine offers milk. Decide on a price for the milk. Then complete the table.

FOOD	PRICE	(quarter)	(dime)	(nickel)
MILK 1 PINT				

Skip Worms

These are Skip Worms. Sara is a 1-Skip Worm. She counts by 1. Sammy is a 2-Skip Worm. He counts by 2. Sadie is a 5-Skip Worm. She counts by 5.

The head of each worm is zero.

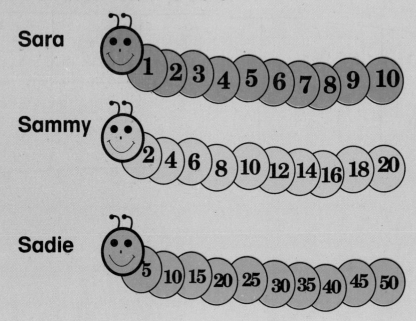

1. How many numbers are on Sammy Skip Worm's body?

   a. 1

   b. 10

   c. 12

2. Which Skip Worm has the greatest number on its tail?

   a. Sara

   b. Sammy

   c. Sadie

3. Sonny is a 4-Skip Worm. What are the first 3 numbers after Sonny's head?

   a. 1, 2, 3

   b. 1, 5, 9

   c. 4, 8, 12

4. Which numbers on Sara are also on Sammy?

5. Name the three numbers that follow 25 on Sadie.

6. Which Skip Worm is good for counting 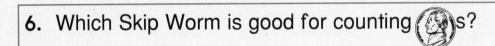s?

7. Sadie is a growing Skip Worm. What do you think will be her greatest number by the end of the school year?

8. Sandra is a new Skip Worm in the neighborhood. What number does she count by? Fill in her numbers.

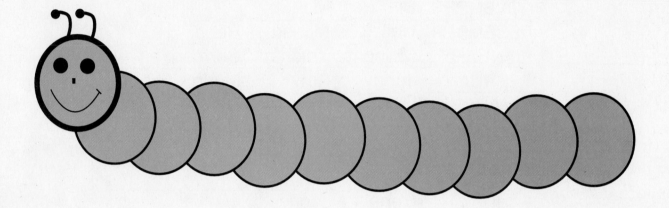

Happy Birthday!

Ms. Maine made a birthday chart for her class. She asked all the students to name the month they were born in.

SEPTEMBER	Judy	Mel	Juan	
OCTOBER	John	Hank	David	
NOVEMBER	Bill	Mary		
DECEMBER	Gail	Marisa	Roger	
JANUARY	Malcom	Yolanda	Carmen	
FEBRUARY	Jenny	Amy	Marie	
MARCH	Gwen	Ryan	Derek	
APRIL	Mark	Frank	Nellie	
MAY	Harry			
JUNE	Justin	Chen		
JULY	Gene	Jean		
AUGUST	Howie	Sara	Tom	Alisa

1. In what month is Marisa's birthday?

   a. January

   b. November

   c. December

2. One month has more birthdays than the others. Which of these students was born in that month?

   a. Malcolm

   b. Sara

   c. Marie

3. Bobby is a new student. He has a birthday in the same month as Harry. What month is Bobby's birthday?

   a. November

   b. May

   c. June

4. How many birthdays are in December?

5. How many students have a birthday in the same month as Carmen?

6. Name a student who has a birthday in the same month as Ryan.

7. Some of the students have birthdays in the summertime. Choose a girl whose birthday is in a summer month. How do you think she celebrates her birthday?

8. Make a birthday chart for your family.

SEPTEMBER	
OCTOBER	
NOVEMBER	
DECEMBER	
JANUARY	
FEBRUARY	
MARCH	
APRIL	
MAY	
JUNE	
JULY	
AUGUST	

Frog Hop

Belinda counted 6 hopping frogs. She gave names to all the frogs that hopped. Then she made a chart of the distances they jumped.

Name	Distance
Emily	22 centimeters
Fred	28 centimeters
Charlie	21 centimeters
Mandy	30 centimeters
Truman	16 centimeters
Nat	28 centimeters

1. How far did Charlie jump?

   a. 16 centimeters

   b. 20 centimeters

   c. 21 centimeters

2. Which frog jumped the farthest?

   a. Mandy

   b. Emily

   c. Nat

3. Besides the hopping frogs, Belinda counted 15 more frogs in the lake. How many frogs did she count in all?

   a. 6

   b. 9

   c. 21

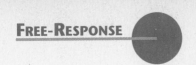

4. Which two frogs jumped the same distance?

5. How much farther did Nat jump than Charlie?

6. After Belinda made her chart, one of the 6 frogs jumped 10 centimeters more. That frog's total distance was 26 centimeters. Which frog was it?

7. Divide the frogs into teams of 3 frogs each. Which team has the greatest total distance?

8. Fred suddenly jumps more than 3 centimeters but less than 10 centimeters. What is Fred's total distance now?

School Colors

Today is Color Day at Midland School. The school colors are green and black. The students are wearing 1 or 2 of the colors. Ms. Lopez puts large green and black circles on the floor of the classroom. She asks her students to stand where they belong. Here are the circles.

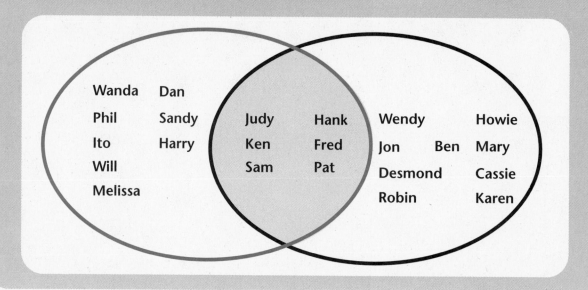

1. What is Melissa wearing?

   a. green

   b. black

   c. green and black

2. Name something that Desmond is not wearing.

   a. a green shirt

   b. black shoes

   c. black pants

3. How many students are wearing BOTH green and black clothes?

   a. 6

   b. 8

   c. 14

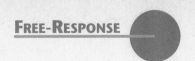

4. How many students are not in the green circle?

5. Ms. Lopez is wearing a black skirt. Put her name in the correct place below.

Wanda	Dan					
Phil	Sandy	Judy	Hank	Wendy		Howie
Ito	Harry	Ken	Fred	Jon	Ben	Mary
Will		Sam	Pat	Desmond		Cassie
Melissa				Robin		Karen

6. Carlos joins the class. He is wearing black socks and a green sweater. Put his name in the correct place below.

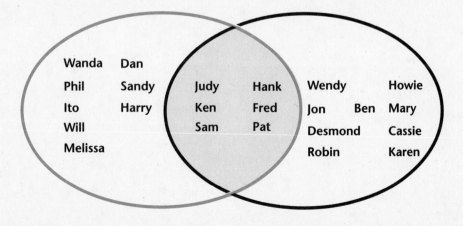

Wanda	Dan					
Phil	Sandy	Judy	Hank	Wendy		Howie
Ito	Harry	Ken	Fred	Jon	Ben	Mary
Will		Sam	Pat	Desmond		Cassie
Melissa				Robin		Karen

7. Would you be in one of these circles today? Why or why not?

8. Draw your own circles for the colors red and blue. Fill in the circles for your class.

Birthday Balloons

Amanda is 3 years old today. Her mother is decorating the house with balloons. In the den, she puts 3 balloons on the front door, 3 on the TV, and 3 on Amanda's toy truck. In the kitchen, she puts 3 more balloons on the window and 3 balloons on the birthday cake.

1. How many different bunches of 3 balloons are there?

   a. 5
   b. 6
   c. 7

3. How many balloons are in the house altogether?

   a. 3
   b. 12
   c. 15

2. Amanda takes the balloons from the kitchen window and puts them on her birthday cake with the other balloons. How many balloons are now on Amanda's cake?

   a. 3
   b. 6
   c. 9

4. Which room has more balloons, the den or the kitchen?

5. Amanda sees 9 balloons in the den. Where are they?

6. The number of balloons in each bunch is the age of the birthday person. Peter finds 12 balloons in each bunch on his birthday. How old is he?

7. Amanda finds more bunches of 3 balloons in the backyard. How many balloons are outside?

8. Amanda's mother finds 4 places to put balloon bunches on your next birthday. How many balloons will she need for you?

Line Up

Mary, Bert, John, Hallie, and Ernie are in the school yard. They decide to line up to compare their heights. John, the shortest, is first in line and is 42 inches tall. Hallie, the tallest, is last in line and is 48 inches tall. Ernie is shorter than Bert. Ernie is taller Mary.

42 inches

48 inches

John   **Hallie**

1. Who is the tallest of these 3 students?

   a. Mary

   b. John

   c. Ernie

2. How many inches taller is Hallie than John?

   a. 6

   b. 8

   c. 42

3. Paul joins the group. He is 49 inches tall. Where should he stand in line?

   a. first

   b. fifth

   c. sixth

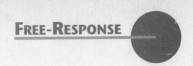

4. A foot is 12 inches. How many feet tall is Hallie?

5. Reread the paragraph at the top of page 54. Show where Bert, Mary, and Ernie are in the line.

6. Is Ernie more than 48 inches tall?

7. Name someone who is taller than Mary.

8. Bert is 45 inches tall. How tall could Ernie and Mary be?

Apple Boxes

Harry, Juanita, and Judy each have a box of 12 apples. The boxes are divided into parts.

Harry's box of apples has 2 parts. Each part is $\frac{1}{2}$.

Juanita's box of apples has 3 parts. Each part is $\frac{1}{3}$.

Judy's box of apples has 4 parts. Each part is $\frac{1}{4}$.

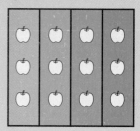

1. How many apples are in each part of Judy's box?

    a. 3

    b. 4

    c. 6

2. How many apples are in each part of Juanita's box?

    a. 3

    b. 4

    c. 6

3. Who has the most apples in one part of the box?

    a. Harry

    b. Juanita

    c. Judy

4. Which has more apples, $\frac{1}{3}$ of a box or $\frac{1}{4}$ of a box?

5. Judy's box has the most parts. Does Judy's box have the most apples?

6. Suppose you take a full part of apples from each box. How many apples would you have in all?

7. Draw lines to show 6 equal parts. How many apples are in each part?

8. Here are 2 boxes of 6 apples. Show 2 different ways to make equal parts.

Stickers

Jeremy has 45 stickers. He buys them in packs of 10. He wants to share his stickers with his friends, Sam and Cathy. Below are the stickers that Jeremy has.

Key

 = 1 pack of stickers

⬤ = 1 sticker

1. How many rows of stickers are in each package?

   a. 2

   b. 8

   c. 10

2. Jeremy counts the stickers 5 at a time. How many groups of 5 are there?

   a. 1

   b. 5

   c. 9

3. Jeremy keeps 15 stickers for himself. How can he give Sam and Cathy the same amount he has?

   a. Give Sam 2 packs and Cathy 1 pack.

   b. Give Sam and Cathy one full pack each and open another pack for them to share.

   c. Give Sam and Cathy one full pack each and have Jeremy keep the last pack for himself.

4. How many people will share the stickers?

5. How many full packs of 10 stickers can each person receive?

6. Will Jeremy use all the loose stickers that are not in a pack?

7. Is it easier to count stickers when they are still in their packs? Why or why not?

8. Jeremy now has 100 stickers. He trades a full 10-pack for one valuable sticker. He does this a few times until he has the stickers he wants. How many stickers does he have when he is finished trading?

Mostly Marbles

Tony and Alex are playing marbles. Each begins with 45 marbles. They will play each other every day for 5 days.

On Monday, Alex wins 14 marbles from Tony. On Tuesday he wins 3 more marbles from Tony. On Wednesday, Tony wins 7 marbles from Alex. On Thursday, no one wins any marbles. On Friday, Alex wins 2 marbles.

I. How many marbles does Tony have at the start of the game?

   a. 0

   b. 22

   c. 45

2. How many marbles does Tony have after Monday's game?

   a. 31

   b. 45

   c. 59

3. If the game stops right after Tuesday's game, what happens?

   a. Tony wins.

   b. Alex wins.

   c. The game is a tie.

4. On which day does each player have the same number of marbles before the game as after the game?

5. What happens to the number of Alex's marbles when Tony wins 7 marbles from him? Does it go up or down?

6. How many of the 5 days does Alex win marbles from Tony?

7. Alex and Tony play their game one more day after Friday. Tony wins the game for the entire week. How many marbles did he win on that day?

8. On Monday of the next week, Tony and Alex start a new game of marbles. They each start with 45 marbles. After Friday's game, Tony has 15 marbles and Alex has 75. Show how this could happen. Write in the chart the number of marbles Tony and Alex have after each game.

	Start	Monday	Tuesday	Wednesday	Thursday	Friday
Tony	45					15
Alex	45					75

In the Neighborhood

Don, Allie, Wendy, and their friends go to Small Creek School. Here is a map of their neighborhood.

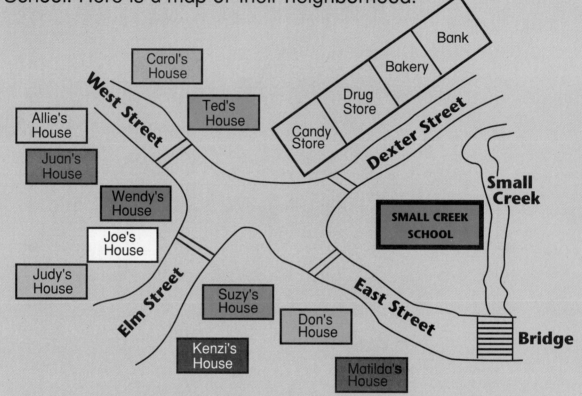

1. Who lives between Allie's house and Wendy's house?

   a. Juan

   b. Ted

   c. Joe

2. Which street must Don cross to go to Small Creek School?

   a. West Street

   b. East Street

   c. Elm Street

3. How can Wendy get to school?

   a. cross Elm Street and then cross Dexter Street

   b. cross West Street and then cross East Street

   c. cross Elm Street and then cross East Street

4. Who lives next door to Ted?

5. How many more houses are there than stores?

6. Which street has a bridge over Small Creek?

7. After school, Don goes to Ted's house and then goes home. Which streets does he cross? Write them in order from first to last.

8. Matilda has a newspaper route. She picks up the papers at the candy store. Then, she delivers one paper to each house and then goes home. Draw a route on the map for Matilda to deliver the papers.

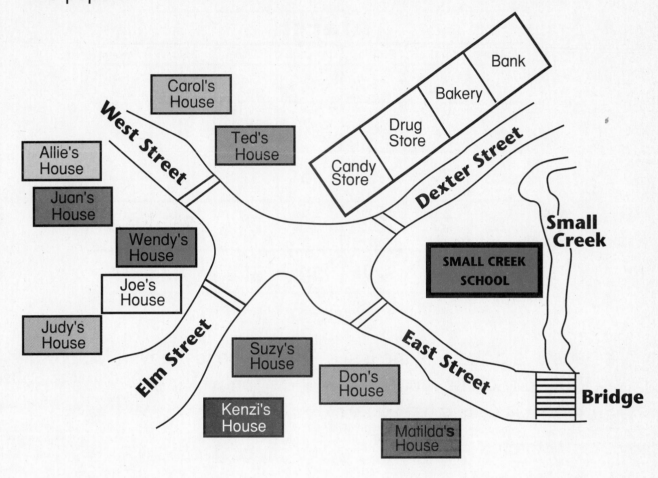

Calendar Days

Jason and his family have many important events in March. They keep a calendar on the refrigerator to remember the dates.

March

Sunday	Monday	Tuesday	Wednesday	Thursday	Friday	Saturday
		1	2	3	4	5
6	7	8	9	10	11	12
13	14	15	16	17	18	19
20	21	22	23	24	25	26
27	28	29	30	31		

I. Jason's birthday is the last Saturday of the month. What is Jason's birth date?

   a. March 5

   b. March 26

   c. March 31

2. How many days are in March?

   a. 26

   b. 31

   c. 33

3. The last day in March falls on which day of the week?

   a. Saturday

   b. Thursday

   c. Friday

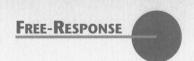

4. Jason works each week from Monday through Friday. How many days does he work in March?

5. Jason's grandparents visit the family every Thursday. How many days in March do they visit?

6. April is the month after March. On which day of the week is April 1?

7. A storm closes the school for 3 days in March. Write which 3 days. On what day do the students return to school?

8. The principal at your school orders some new playground equipment on March I. The new equipment will take at least 3 weeks to arrive. On what date will the new equipment arrive?

Class Monitors

Mrs. Brill's classroom has 16 students in it. Students take turns as class monitors each month. They take care of paper, books, the chalkboard, erasers, and the plants. Here is a chart of jobs for February.

February Monitors				
	Week 1	**Week 2**	**Week 3**	**Week 4**
paper	Allan	Sam	Ronnie	Tom
books	Sonia	Ann	Jenny	Fran
chalkboard	Jo	Harry	Juan	Allan
erasers	Phil	Miriam	Tania	Angela
plants	Shana	Tom	Harry	Sonia

1. How many jobs have to be filled in February?

    a. 4

    b. 10

    c. 20

2. Who is the eraser monitor for Week 3?

    a. Phil

    b. Harry

    c. Tania

3. What job is Sonia assigned in Week 4?

    a. plant monitor

    b. paper monitor

    c. book monitor

4. Allan has more than one job for the month. Name another student with more than one job.

5. How many different students are monitors?

6. How many students have only one job in February?

7. Ruth joins the class during the first week of February. She can choose one of Allan's jobs. Which does she pick?

8. In March, Angela will be a monitor two times. She will take a job different from her February job. Name Angela's two jobs for March.

School Store

The school store has small objects for students to buy.

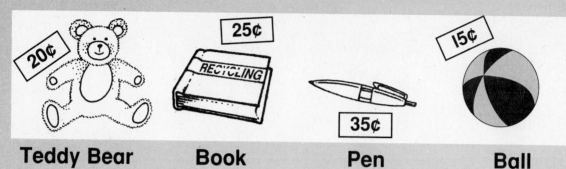

Teddy Bear   **Book**   **Pen**   **Ball**

I. Which object costs I quarter?

   a. book

   b. pen

   c. teddy bear

2. How much do 2 pens cost?

   a. 60¢

   b. 65¢

   c. 70¢

3. Joshua spends

   What does he buy?

   a. book

   b. ball

   c. pen

4. What is the cost of the teddy bear?

5. Amy spends exactly 60¢ for 2 presents. What does she buy?

6. How many balls can you buy with these coins?

7. On the graph, color the [   ] to show the cost of each object. Use a different color for each object.

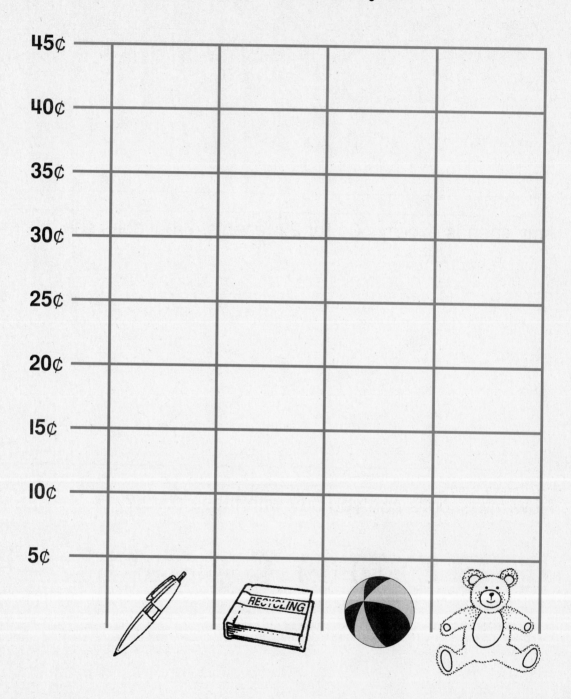

8. Write I thing to buy at the school store. Draw the coins you need to buy it.

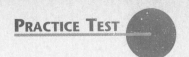

You've had lots of practice doing math. Now you're ready to take a test. This test has problems just like the ones you've been working out all along. So turn the page and see what you can do.

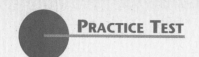

Getting to School

Mr. Diaz is making a chart of how the second-grade students get to school. He uses different color rectangles for each group. Each ☐ stands for a student who walks to school. Each ☐ stands for a student who takes the bus. Each ☐ stands for a student who rides a car to school. Here is Mr. Diaz's chart.

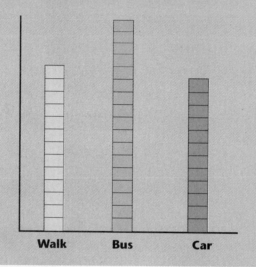

Walk   Bus   Car

I. Megan walks to school. Which rectangle stands for her?

a. ☐

b. ☐

c. ☐

2. How do most of the students get to school?

a. walk

b. bus

c. car

3. Half the students who travel by car stay after school for music lessons. How many students stay for music?

a. 5

b. 6

c. 12

4. More students walk than travel by car. How many more?

5. There is a parade this morning and the roads are filled with traffic. Which group of students will not be late?

6. Keith decides to walk to school instead of taking the bus. How do most of the students get to school now?

7. Sida joins the class. In the morning, she takes the bus to school. In the afternoon, she goes home by car. How can Mr. Diaz show Sida on the chart?

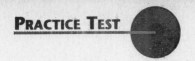
8. One day Paula walks to school and arrives on time. On the same day Richard rides the bus to school and is late. How can this happen?

Pennies a Day

Allison's grandmother gives her pennies for 2 weeks. On Sunday, Allison gets I penny. On each day after that, her grandmother gives her 2 more pennies than the day before.

	Sunday	Monday	Tuesday	Wednesday	Thursday	Friday	Saturday
Week I	Sunday I penny	Monday 3 pennies	Tuesday 5 pennies	Wednesday	Thursday	Friday	Saturday
Week 2	Sunday I penny	Monday 3 pennies	Tuesday 5 pennies	Wednesday	Thursday	Friday	Saturday

I. How many more pennies does Allison get each day?

a. I

b. 2

c. 3

2. On which day does Allison receive 7 pennies?

a. Wednesday

b. Thursday

c. Saturday

3. How many pennies does Allison get on the second Saturday?

a. 14

b. 27

c. 50

4. On which day does Allison have the least number of pennies?

5. How many days does Allison's grandmother give her pennies?

6. Allison saves each penny her grandmother gives her. Tell the number of pennies Allison has after 5 days.

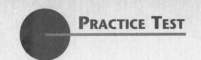

7. At the end of two weeks, Allison decides to spend her pennies in a pattern. On the chart, write how many pennies Allison spends each day.

	Sunday	Monday	Tuesday	Wednesday	Thursday	Friday	Saturday
Week 1							
Week 2	Sunday	Monday	Tuesday	Wednesday	Thursday	Friday	Saturday

8. After two weeks, Allison's grandmother chooses another pattern for giving pennies away. Think of a new pattern and write it in the chart below.

Sunday	Monday	Tuesday	Wednesday	Thursday	Friday	Saturday